ADVENTUROUS OLIVIA'S CALM QUEST

by Florenza Denise Lee

Illustrated and designed by Fx and Color Studio

Published titles by Florenza are:

Adventurous Olivia's Alphabet Quest

Barry Bear's Very Best, Learning to Say No to Negative Influences

If…The Story of Faith Walker

There's No Place Like My Own Home

The Tail of Max the Mindless Dog, A Children's Book on Mindfulness

Welcome Home Daddy, Love, Lexi

Children's Books coming soon are:

Acornsville, Land of the Secret Seed Keepers

Adventurous Olivia's Numerical Quest

Amiri's Birthday Wish

Micah and Malik's Super Awesome Excellent Adventure

Oh, My Goodness, Look at this Big Mess

Two Bees in a Hive

When Life Gives Us Wind

Young Reader Chapter Books coming soon are:

Hoku to the Rescue

Two-Thirds is a Whole

For more information regarding Florenza's books, or to contact her to speak at your school or event,

please visit www. wordstoponderpublishing.com

Dedication

I dedicate this book to all the adventurers in the world.

This Book Belongs To:

_____

Hello, it's me, Olivia! Mom calls me Adventurous Olivia. I don't know what an adventurer does but I am on a quest to find out. Do you want to join me? Then, let's go!

Where shall we look first? Here?
What about over there?
Should we search under this?
How about behind that?

"Olivia!!!!"

Oh, Oh! I recognize that tone.

"Yes, Ma'am?"

"I have an adventure for you. It is a quest to locate your calm."

"Yes, Ma'am, I certainly will!"

Let's go!

Where might we find our calm?

We have looked everywhere, and
we still cannot locate an adventure!
What are we forgetting?

Think! Think!

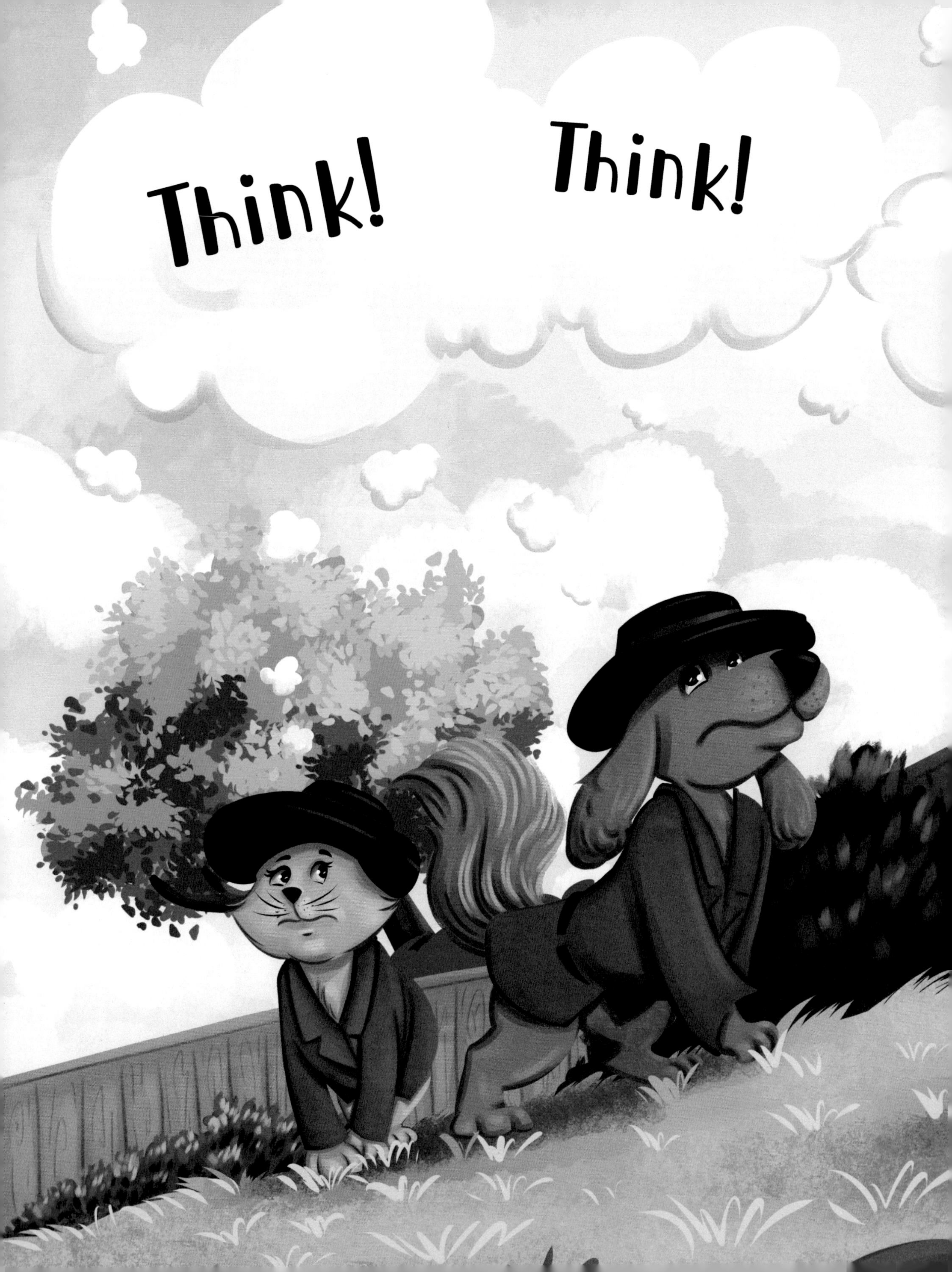

Dad says when I feel anxious,
I should pause and meditate.

First, let's find a comfortable place
to sit or lay down. This looks like a perfect spot!
The grass is soft and prickly.
What does it feel like where you are sitting?
Dad says this is awareness; we are focusing.

Breathe in and out. Do you feel the air
entering your nose? Inhaling makes my belly go up, and
exhaling makes it go down. As I breathe in, the air is cool.
When I breathe out, it is warm.

In. Out. Pause.
In. Out. Pause.

Let your belly rise and fall.

Follow the air from your nose down to your toes.
From the bottom of your feet, all the way back up to
the top of your head.

In. Out. Pause.

In. Out. Pause.

Sometimes silly thoughts jump into my head like scampering squirrels! When that happens, Dad says to just let them pass right on by. You don't need to chase them; notice them, but don't respond.

Let your belly
rise and fall.

"Thank you, eyes, for seeing."

"Thank you, mouth, for meowing."

Meditating is a perfect time to be kind to yourself.
I thank every part of my body from my itty-bitty toes to my little
button nose. "Let your attitude be gratitude!"

Let your belly rise
and fall.

Open your eyes. We did it! We've
located our calm! How do you feel?
I feel great! Now, let's go on to
our next adventure!

ABOUT THE AUTHOR

FLORENZA LEE is the author of interactive, engaging Children's books focusing on Social Emotional Learning. She is also a publisher, narrative coach, speaker, radio talk show host, Master Storyteller, wife, and mother. Florenza and her husband, CSM (Ret US Army) Trefus Lee, have been married for nearly 38 years and reside in Hampton, Virginia. Their daughters, Jessica and Missy, call Las Vegas, Nevada, and Hampton, Virginia, home.

Made in the USA
Middletown, DE
09 July 2022

68889853R00022